A COMIC BOOK ADAPTATION
OF SVEN HASSEL'S CLASSIC WWII NOVEL
ILLUSTRATED BY JOHAN JERNHED

SVEN HASSEL

LEGION OF THE DAMNED

BOOK ONE

ISBN 9788771661781

www.SvenHassel.com

CHAPTER 1

FILTHY DESERTER

"WELL, YOUR FIVE MINUTES ARE UP. TIME TO FACE
THE CONSEQUENCES!"

HE PRESSED THE BUZZER. TWO LARGE SS-MEN IN
BLACK UNIFORMS WALKED IN. A QUICK ORDER - AND
THEY DRAGGED EVA TO A LEATHER-COVERED TABLE.

5

CHAPTER 2

**THEY DIED BY DAY,
THEY DIED BY NIGHT**

WE WERE CHAINED TOGETHER, TWO BY TWO, WITH
HANDCUFFS AND SHACKLES ON OUR ANKLES, AND
LASTLY, A CHAIN WAS RUN AROUND THE WHOLE DE-
TACHMENT. WE WERE DRIVEN TO THE GOODS STATION,
GUARDED BY HEAVILY ARMED MILITARY POLICE.

WE WERE IN THE TRAIN FOR THREE DAYS AND
NIGHTS…

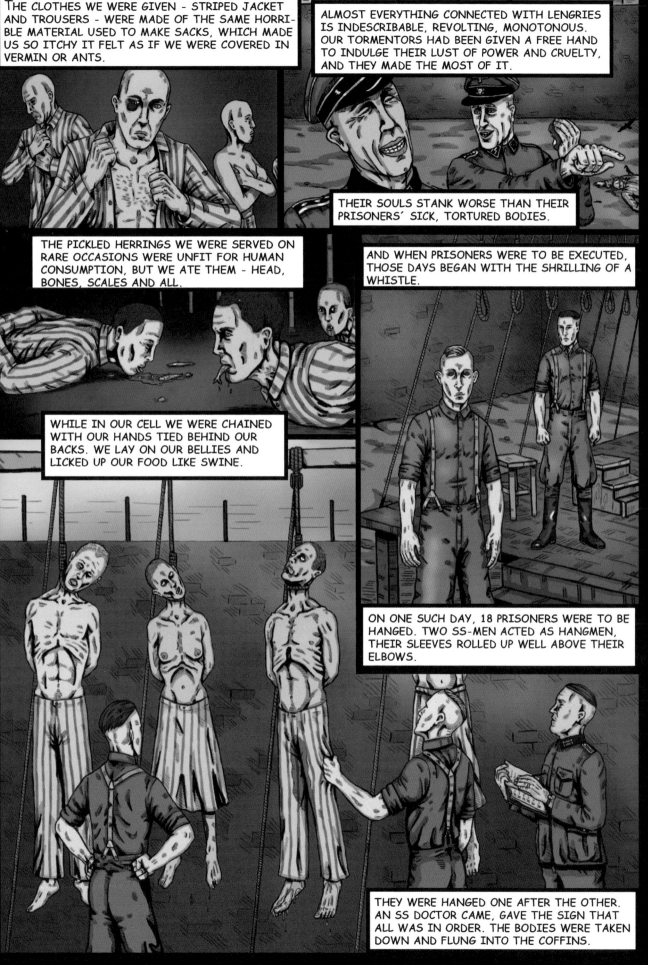

THE CLOTHES WE WERE GIVEN - STRIPED JACKET AND TROUSERS - WERE MADE OF THE SAME HORRIBLE MATERIAL USED TO MAKE SACKS, WHICH MADE US SO ITCHY IT FELT AS IF WE WERE COVERED IN VERMIN OR ANTS.

ALMOST EVERYTHING CONNECTED WITH LENGRIES IS INDESCRIBABLE, REVOLTING, MONOTONOUS. OUR TORMENTORS HAD BEEN GIVEN A FREE HAND TO INDULGE THEIR LUST OF POWER AND CRUELTY, AND THEY MADE THE MOST OF IT.

THEIR SOULS STANK WORSE THAN THEIR PRISONERS' SICK, TORTURED BODIES.

THE PICKLED HERRINGS WE WERE SERVED ON RARE OCCASIONS WERE UNFIT FOR HUMAN CONSUMPTION, BUT WE ATE THEM - HEAD, BONES, SCALES AND ALL.

AND WHEN PRISONERS WERE TO BE EXECUTED, THOSE DAYS BEGAN WITH THE SHRILLING OF A WHISTLE.

WHILE IN OUR CELL WE WERE CHAINED WITH OUR HANDS TIED BEHIND OUR BACKS. WE LAY ON OUR BELLIES AND LICKED UP OUR FOOD LIKE SWINE.

ON ONE SUCH DAY, 18 PRISONERS WERE TO BE HANGED. TWO SS-MEN ACTED AS HANGMEN, THEIR SLEEVES ROLLED UP WELL ABOVE THEIR ELBOWS.

THEY WERE HANGED ONE AFTER THE OTHER. AN SS DOCTOR CAME, GAVE THE SIGN THAT ALL WAS IN ORDER. THE BODIES WERE TAKEN DOWN AND FLUNG INTO THE COFFINS.

11

EXCELLENT! THAT'S HOW YOU OBEY AN ORDER. NOW, DROP ON YOUR KNEES AND REPEAT AFTER ME.

LOUD AND CLEAR: WE ARE SWINE AND TRAITORS!

WE ARE SWINE AND TRAITORS!

WHO ARE TO BE DESTROYED!

WHO ARE TO BE DESTROYED.

AND THAT'S WHAT WE DESERVE!

AND THAT'S WHAT WE DESERVE.

KÄTHE RAGNER WAS IN THE CELL NEXT TO MINE. SHE LOOKED DREADFUL.

THE WHORE'S BROKEN HER NECK!

WHY ARE YOU LOOKING AT ME LIKE THAT? HOW OLD DO YOU THINK I AM? WELL OVER 50, I SUPPOSE YOU'D SAY. NEXT MONTH I TURN 23. TWENTY MONTHS AGO, A MAN GUESSED THAT I WAS 18.

KÄTHE GOT INVOLVED WITH A YOUNG CAPTAIN, AND THEY GOT ENGAGED. HE WAS ARRESTED, AND 4 DAYS LATER THEY CAME FOR HER AS WELL. SHE DIDN'T UNDERSTAND WHY AT THE TIME, BUT WAS SENTENCED TO 10 YEARS. SHE THEN WITNESSED HER FIANCÉ'S EXECUTION, BEFORE BEING SENT TO LENGRIES.

ONE MORNING KÄTHE AND 3 OTHER WOMEN WERE ORDERED TO CRAWL DOWN A STEEP, LONG FLIGHT OF STAIRS. IT WAS A TYPE OF EXERCISE THAT THE GUARDS LIKED TO TREAT US WITH.

I DON'T KNOW WHETHER KÄTHE FELL, OR LET HERSELF DROP FROM THE 5TH FLOOR.

CHAPTER 3

FAGEN

A FEW DAYS AFTER KÄTHE´S DEATH, A NUMBER OF US
WERE TRANSFERRED TO THE FAGEN IMPRISONMENT
CAMP CLOSE TO BREMEN. THEY TOLD US THAT WE
WERE BEING ASSIGNED 'SPECIAL WORK OF EXTRAOR-
DINARY IMPORTANCE´.

WHAT TYPE OF WORK LAY AHEAD DID NOT REALLY IN-
TEREST US. NONE OF US BELIEVED IT WOULD BE ANY
DIFFERENT THAN WHAT WE HAD GROWN ACCUSTOMED
TO. WE WERE USED TO WORKING AS DRAUGHT ANIMALS
PULLING A PLOUGH, HARROW, ROLLER OR WAGON,
TILL YOU DROPPED DEAD. WE WERE USED TO WORKING
IN A QUARRY, TILL YOU DROPPED DEAD. WE ALSO
WORKED IN THE JUTE MILL, WHERE YOU DROPPED
DEAD WITH THE ADDED BONUS OF HAEMORRHAGED
LUNGS.
ALL WORK WAS THE SAME: YOU DROPPED DEAD FROM
IT.

WE WORKED LIKE GALLEY SLAVES, DIGGING SAND FROM 05:00 IN THE MORNING TO 18:00 IN THE EVENING...

THE CAMP COMMANDER INFORMED US THAT THOSE WHO VOLUNTEERED TO DISMANTLE BOMBS HAD A CHANCE OF BEING PARDONED. YOU HAD TO DISMANTLE 15 BOMBS FOR EVERY YEAR OF YOUR SENTENCE.

FAGEN WORKED ON TWO FRONTS, AS IT WERE; IT WAS REALLY A CAMP OF EXPERIMENTAL MEDICINE, BUT THERE WERE ALSO THE BOMBS.

SOME PEOPLE HAD MANAGED TO DO 50 BEFORE THEY WERE KILLED, BUT I ARGUED THAT SOONER OR LATER SOMEONE MUST GET UP TO 225, SO I VOLUNTEERED.

THE BOMBS HAD TO BE FREED OF DIRT; A WIRE HAD TO BE PLACED ROUND THEM AND DERRICKS LOWERED THEM INTO THE HOLES, THEN THEY HAD TO BE HOISTED ONE MILLIMETRE AT A TIME, UNTIL THEY WERE UPRIGHT.

ONLY ONE MAN KEPT THE BOMB COMPANY, AND THAT WAS THE PRISONER WHO WAS TO UNSCREW THE FUSE. IF HE BUNGLED IT...

WE KEPT A COUPLE OF WOODEN BOXES IN THE WORKSHOP LORRY FOR THOSE WHO DID BUNGLE AND EXPLODED WITH THE BOMBS, BUT IT WAS NOT EVERY DAY THAT THEY WERE NEEDED - NOT THAT PEOPLE DIDN'T MESS-UP, BUT BECAUSE WE COULDN'T ALWAYS FIND ANY PIECES OF THEM LEFT TO PUT INTO BOXES.

MY 68TH BOMB WAS AN AERIAL TORPEDO, AND IT TOOK US 15 HOURS TO DIG FREE.

WHEN WE HAD DUG IT FREE WE WERE TOLD THAT THE FUSE WAS NOT TO BE RE-MOVED UNTIL THE TORPEDO HAD BEEN TAKEN OUT OF TOWN.

SUCH AN AERIAL TORPEDO IS A COLD-BLOODED OPPONENT; IT GIVES NOTHING AWAY, ABSOLUTELY NOTHING. YOU CANNOT PLAY POKER WITH AN AERIAL TORPEDO.

THIS PROBABLY MEANT THAT THE TORPEDO WAS DIFFERENT FROM THE ONES THEY HAD SEEN IN THE PAST.

IT TOOK US 4 HOURS TO HOIST THE BOMB UP WITH THE DER-RICK, LOWER IT INTO PLACE AND SECURE IT SO THAT IT COULD NOT MOVE.

YOU! CAN YOU DRIVE? UP YOU GO!

WHO KNOWS HOW TO DRIVE?

I DON'T KNOW WHAT I WAS THINKING OF DURING THAT DRIVE. I ONLY KNEW THAT THERE WAS PLENTY OF TIME TO THINK, AND THAT I WAS CALM, A LITTLE EXCITED PERHAPS, EVEN A LITTLE HAPPY FOR THE FIRST TIME IN A VERY LONG WHILE.

WHEN YOU DON'T KNOW IF THE NEXT SECOND/BREATH/MOMENT WILL BE YOUR LAST, YOU HAVE PLENTY OF TIME TO REFLECT.

I HAD LOST SIGHT OF MYSELF, HAD CEASED TO HAVE AN OPINION OF MYSELF, MY PERSONALITY HAD BEEN SQUASHED - AND YET IT HAD SURVIVED THE DAILY DEGRADATION. HERE YOU ARE, I SAID TO MYSELF. GOOD DAY TO YOU. HERE YOU STAND. DOING WHAT OTHERS DID NOT DARE TO DO.

I COULD PERHAPS HAVE ESCAPED; THERE HAD BEEN MANY OPPORTUNITIES IN THE EMPTY STREETS.

TWELVE KILOMETRES OUT ON THE HEATH I WAS ABLE TO STOP. AS THEY CONSIDERED IT IMPOSSIBLE TO UNLOAD THE TORPEDO, IT WAS EXPLODED IN ITS SPRUNG DERRICK.

WHY DIDN'T I TAKE THE CHANCE WHEN I HAD IT? I DON'T KNOW. BUT I DIDN'T. I WAS STRANGELY ENJOYING MYSELF AND THIS SOLITUDE MY DEAR AERIAL TORPEDO AND I WERE SHARING. NOBODY COULD TOUCH ME.

FOR DRIVING IT, I WAS GIVEN 3 CIGARETTES WITH THE USUAL REMARK THAT I HAD NOT DESERVED THEM, BUT WAS GIVEN THEM BECAUSE THE FÜHRER WAS NOT DEVOID OF HUMAN FEELINGS.

AND THEN THE WORST THING THAT COULD HAPPEN TO A PRISONER HAPPENED TO ME - I FELL ILL; YET THAT PERHAPS SAVED MY LIFE. IF YOU REPORTED SICK YOU WERE AT ONCE SENT TO THE CAMP HOSPITAL, WHERE THEY EXPERIMENTED ON YOU, TILL YOU COULD BE USED NO MORE; AND YOU COULD ONLY BE USED NO MORE WHEN YOU WERE DEAD FROM HAVING BEEN USED. THEREFORE, YOU DID NOT REPORT SICK. BUT DURING A ROLL-CALL I COLLAPSED.

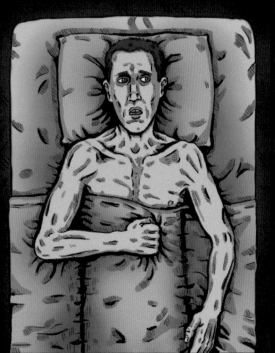

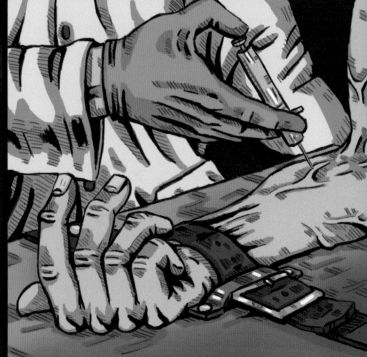

THERE, A GRINNING SS MAN TOLD ME THAT I HAD BEEN TAKEN OFF THE BOMB-DISPOSAL WORK. THE BOMBS I HAD DISMANTLED NO LONGER COUNTED.

I WAS LUCKIER THAN MOST. ONE DAY THEY THOUGHT I HAD HAD ENOUGH, OR PERHAPS I WAS NOT INTERESTING ANY-MORE AND I WAS RETURNED TO CAMP.

I WAS SENT BACK TO LENGRIES, AND EVERYTHING I'D BEEN THROUGH HAD BEEN FOR NOTHING. SEVEN MONTHS IN THE GRAVEL-PITS AT LENGRIES PROVED TO BE A MONOTONOUS, LETHARGIC IN-SANITY.

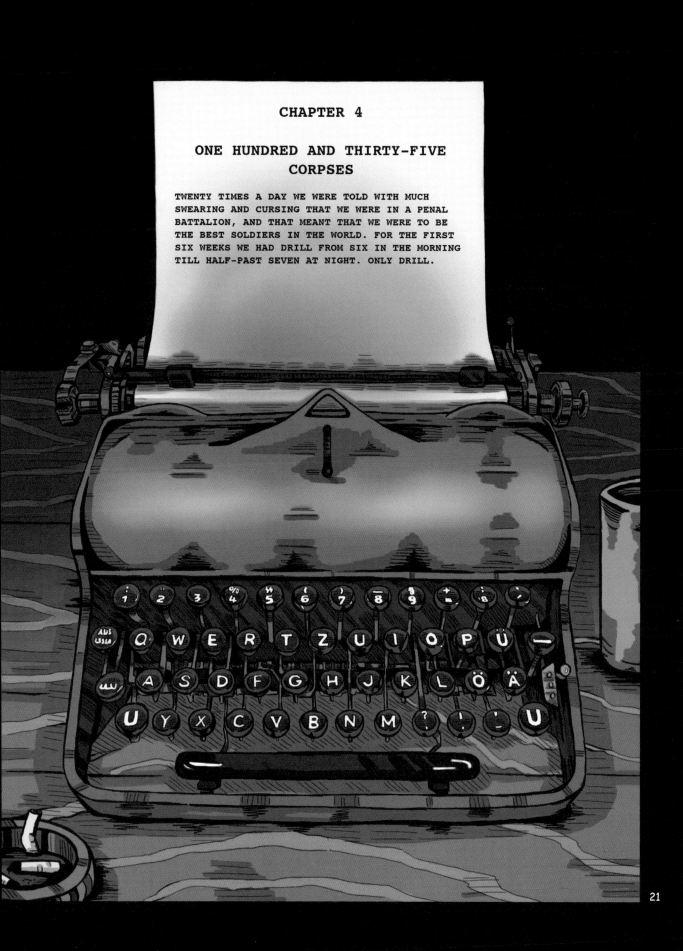

CHAPTER 4

ONE HUNDRED AND THIRTY-FIVE CORPSES

TWENTY TIMES A DAY WE WERE TOLD WITH MUCH SWEARING AND CURSING THAT WE WERE IN A PENAL BATTALION, AND THAT MEANT THAT WE WERE TO BE THE BEST SOLDIERS IN THE WORLD. FOR THE FIRST SIX WEEKS WE HAD DRILL FROM SIX IN THE MORNING TILL HALF-PAST SEVEN AT NIGHT. ONLY DRILL.

OUR NCOS WERE A PACK OF HOWLING DEVILS, WHO SHOUTED AND BAWLED AT US TILL WE WERE ON THE VERGE OF MADNESS. THEY NEVER MISSED AN OPPORTUNITY.

WE HAD TO BE IN OUR BUNKS BY 9 PM. BUT THAT WAS NOT THE SAME AS BEING ABLE TO SLEEP. EVERY SINGLE NIGHT THERE WERE DRILL ALERTS AND PRACTICE IN QUICK UNIFORM CHANGE.

ONCE THE FIRST 6 WEEKS WERE COMPLETED WE BEGAN RIFLE PRACTICE AND FIELD EXERCISES. WHICH TRULY TAUGHT US THE MEANING OF FATIGUE.

NO. 3 COMPANY - FALL - IN! WHY IN HELL ARE YOU STINKING PIMPS NOT DOWN ON THE SQUARE YET? AND YOUR BUNKS AREN'T MADE!? DO YOU THINK THIS IS AN OLD PEOPLE'S HOME? LAZY CAMELS!

OUR COMPANY COMMANDER, ONE-ARMED CAPTAIN LOPEI, STOOD SURVEYING US WITH A SLIGHT SMILE AROUND HIS MOUTH. HE REQUIRED IRON DISCIPLINE OF HIS COMPANY, INHUMAN DISCIPLINE; YET WE THOUGHT THAT HE, OUT OF ALL OUR TORMENTORS, HAD SOMETHING HUMAN ABOUT HIM.

IN A PENAL REGIMENT, ALL SINGING AND CONVERSATION IS FORBIDDEN; FOURTH-RATE PEOPLE CANNOT ENJOY THE PRIVILEGES OF THE GERMAN SOLDIER.

HE AT LEAST HAD THE DECENCY TO DO EVERYTHING THAT HE MADE US DO, AND HE NEVER EXPECTED US TO DO WHAT HE COULD NOT HIMSELF. SO, HE WAS FAIR, SOMETHING WE WERE NOT ACCUSTOMED TO; WE WERE USED TO THE PERSON IN AUTHORITY PICKING A SCAPEGOAT, A POOR WRETCH WHOM HE WAS ALWAYS AFTER, NEVER LEAVING HIM ALONE TILL HE WAS DONE FOR, COLLAPSED, DISABLED, KILLED WITH FATIGUE OR DRIVEN TO SUICIDE. IF THAT MAN'S COURAGE AND FAIRNESS HAD NOT BEEN HITCHED TO HITLER'S WAGON, I WOULD HAVE LIKED HIM. AS IT WAS, I RESPECTED HIM.

WHAT IN HELL IS THIS COLLECTION OF FILTHY MONGRELS YOU HAVE HERE? WHAT UNDISCIPLINED RABBLE IS THIS? YOU WOULDN'T THINK THEY WERE PRUSSIAN SOLDIERS. YOU'D THINK THEY WERE MANGY MONGRELS. BUT THAT CAN BE CURED!

ON WE MARCHED, KILOMETRE AFTER KILOMETRE. I BELIEVE THAT I KNOW EVERYTHING WORTH KNOWING ABOUT ROADS: SOFT, HARD, WIDE, NARROW, STONY, MUDDY, CEMENTED, BOGGY, SNOWY, HILLY, GRAVELLED, SLIPPERY, DUSTY ROADS. MY FEET HAVE TAUGHT ME EVERYTHING WORTH KNOWING ABOUT ROADS, CALLOUS ENEMIES AND TORMENTORS OF MY FEET.

THE PICTURE OF OUR TRAINING REQUIRES ONE FINISHING TOUCH. TO PUT EVERYTHING IN ITS PROPER LIGHT AND PERSPECTIVE YOU MUST ADD A KEY INGRE-DIENT: HUNGER.

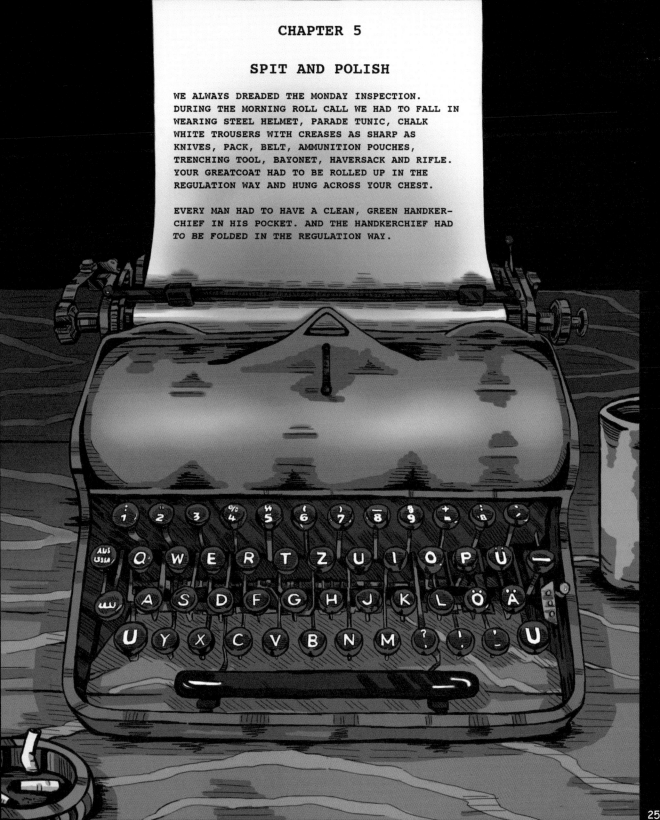

CHAPTER 5

SPIT AND POLISH

WE ALWAYS DREADED THE MONDAY INSPECTION.
DURING THE MORNING ROLL CALL WE HAD TO FALL IN
WEARING STEEL HELMET, PARADE TUNIC, CHALK
WHITE TROUSERS WITH CREASES AS SHARP AS
KNIVES, PACK, BELT, AMMUNITION POUCHES,
TRENCHING TOOL, BAYONET, HAVERSACK AND RIFLE.
YOUR GREATCOAT HAD TO BE ROLLED UP IN THE
REGULATION WAY AND HUNG ACROSS YOUR CHEST.

EVERY MAN HAD TO HAVE A CLEAN, GREEN HANDKER-
CHIEF IN HIS POCKET. AND THE HANDKERCHIEF HAD
TO BE FOLDED IN THE REGULATION WAY.

CHAPTER 6

ONE KIND OF SOLDIER

THE COMMANDANT THEN HANDED THE COMPANY OVER TO THE CHAPLAIN.

"NO. 3 COMPANY – FOR PRAYERS – KNEEL!!" ROARED THE CHAPLAIN.

OUR TRAINING ENDED WITH AN EXERCISE THAT LASTED 7 DAYS AND SLEEPLESS NIGHTS. IT TOOK PLACE ON A HUGE TRAINING AREA CALLED SENNELAGER.

ONE GAME CONSISTED OF DIGGING HOLES JUST DEEP ENOUGH FOR US TO BE BELOW THE SURFACE; THEN HEAVY TANKS CAME UP AND DROVE OVER THE HOLES, WHILE WE COWERED IN THEM, SHAKING WITH FEAR OF BEING CRUSHED.

THIS 'THRILL' WAS IMMEDIATELY FOLLOWED BY ANOTHER. WE HAD TO FLING OURSELVES FLAT ON THE GROUND AND LET THE TANKS DRIVE OVER US.

AT ANY RATE WE WERE SCARED, AND THAT WOULD BE NORMAL. THE GERMAN SOLDIER IS BROUGHT UP ON FEAR, TRAINED TO REACT LIKE A MACHINE THROUGH SHEER TERROR, NOT TO FIGHT BRAVELY BECAUSE HE IS DRIVEN BY A GREAT IDEAL THAT MAKES IT SELF-EVIDENT TO SACRIFICE HIMSELF IF THE NEED ARISES.

CHAPTER 7

OUR FIRST MEETING

"IS THIS COMPANY TO BE BURDENED WITH MORE OF
YOU BLOODY CRIMINALS? DISGUSTING! DON'T LET ME
CATCH YOU COMMITTING THE SLIGHTEST IRREGULARI-
TY, OR I WILL HAVE YOU SENT BACK TO THE GAOL
WHERE YOU OUGHT TO HAVE HAD THE DECENCY TO DIE
LONG AGO, DEVIL TAKE ME IF I DON'T. GAOL'S THE
PLACE FOR YOUR SORT."
SUCH WAS THE GREETING WITH WHICH I WAS WEL-
COMED BY THE COMMANDER OF NO. 5 COMPANY, FAT
HAUPTMANN MEIER, TORMENTOR OF RECRUITS. BUT
ONE WAS SO USED TO THAT SORT OF THING. I WAS
ASSIGNED TO NO. 2 SQUADRON UNDER LEUTNANT VON
BARRING, AND HERE THINGS THAT I WAS NOT ACCUS-
TOMED TO STARTED TO HAPPEN.

WELCOME, LAD, WELCOME TO NO. 5 COMPANY. YOU'VE COME TO A HELLISH AWFUL REGIMENT, BUT WE HAVE TO STICK TOGETHER AND MAKE IT WORK. GO ACROSS THERE TO TRUCK NO. 24 AND REPORT TO UNTEROFFIZIER BEIER, HE IS LEADER OF NO. 1 SECTION.

HERR UNTEROFFIZIER, I BEG...

BUT I GOT NO FURTHER. TWO OF THE 4 LEAPED OFF THE BUCKETS ON WHICH THEY WERE SITTING AND STOOD STIFF AS RAMRODS.

SCHMACK!

WHAT IN ACTUAL HELL? I THINK HITLER'S HAUNTING YOU. WHAT COULD HAVE POSSESSED A FLAT-FOOTED DUNG-BEETLE LIKE YOU TO COME AND INTERRUPT PEACE-LOVING BURGHERS AT THEIR INNOCENT OCCUPATIONS? WHO AND WHAT ARE YOU?

HERR OBERGEFREITER, I COME DIRECTLY FROM LEUTNANT VON BARRING AND AM TO REPORT TO NO. 1 SECTION TO UNTEROFFIZIER BEIER, FOR DUTY.

DID YOU HEAR HIM! HERR OBERGEFREITER. HO, HO, HO! HERR UNTEROFFIZIER BEIER, HA, HA, HA!

HONOURABLE EXCELLENCY! YOUR WORSHIPFUL GRACE, YOUR CAPTIVATING MAGNIFICENCE, HERR UNTEROFFIZIER BEIER, I BEG TO REPORT...

WHERE DID YOU COME FROM?

PENAL BATTALION IN HANOVER.

OFF WITH YOUR WOODEN LEGS! PENAL BATTALION IN HANOVER... THOUGHT YOU WERE TRYING TO MAKE FOOLS OF US CLASHING YOUR HEELS TOGETHER LIKE THAT; BUT I SUPPOSE IT'S A MIRACLE YOU STILL HAVE THEM TO CLASH.

WITH THOSE WORDS I WAS RECEIVED INTO NO 5 COMPANY, AND AN HOUR LATER WE WERE ROLLING ALONG TOWARDS FREIBURG, WHERE WE WERE TO BE FORMED INTO A FIGHTING UNIT AND SENT TO ONE PLACE OR ANOTHER IN CRAZY EUROPE FOR SPECIAL TRAINING. AS WE RATTLED ALONG, MY 4 COMPANIONS INTRODUCED THEMSELVES.

WILLIE BEIER, **THE OLD UN**, WAS LIKE A FATHER TO US. HE WAS ONLY 10 YEARS OUR SENIOR BUT RADIATED A CALM WE ALL DESPERATELY NEEDED, AND MANY WAS THE TIME I REJOICED IN MY GOOD FORTUNE IN BEING PUT IN HIS TANK. HE WAS MARRIED AND HAD 2 CHILDREN. BY TRADE HE WAS A JOINER, AND HIS HOME WAS IN BERLIN. HIS POLITICS HAD EARNED HIM **18 MONTHS** IN A CONCENTRATION CAMP, AFTER WHICH HE HAD BEEN 'PARDONED' AND SENT TO A PENAL REGIMENT.

JOSEPH **PORTA**, OBERGEFREITER "BY GOD'S MERCY," DIDN´T CARE A FIG ABOUT THE WAR, AND I BELIEVE HE WAS EQUALLY FEARED BY GOD, THE DEVIL, AND ALL THE OFFICERS. HE WAS HIGHLY MUSICAL, WITH A ROGUISH HUMOUR, READY TONGUE AND INCREDIBLE CHEEK. THE TRUE GIFT OF A STORYTELLER WAS ALSO HIS. DESPITE HIS "UNIQUE" APPEARANCE HE HAD GREAT SUCCESS WITH WOMEN. HANGING SOCIAL-DEMOCRAT FLAGS ON THE TOWER OF THE MICHAELIS CHURCH HAD HIM ACCUSED OF COMMUNIST ACTIVITIES. HE WAS SENTENCED TO **12 YEARS´** HARD LABOUR, THEN PARDONED AND TOSSED INTO THE PENAL REGIMENT.

"PLUTO," STABSGEFREITER, REAL NAME GUSTAV EICKEN, FORMER DOCKER FROM HAMBURG; IN PRISON THREE TIMES - AND IT WAS NOT FOR POLITICS BUT GOOD HONEST CRIME. THE LAST TIME, HE WAS CHARGED WITH STEALING A LORRY-LOAD OF FLOUR. PLUTO KNEW NOTHING WHAT-SOEVER ABOUT IT, BUT THEY BEAT HIM UP JUST THE SAME. A 12-MINUTE TRIAL EARNED HIM 6 YEARS. AFTER JUST 2 IN FÜHLSBÜTTEL HE ENDED UP INVADING POLAND IN THE 27TH (PENAL) REGIMENT.

OBERGEFREITER ANTON STEYER, ALSO CALLED "MIDGET" BECAUSE OF HIS 152 CM HEIGHT. HE WAS A WHIPPER-SNAPPER FROM COLOGNE, WHERE HE HAD WORKED IN THE PERFUME BUSINESS. A RATHER NOISY DECLARATION OF THOUGHTS IN A BIER-STUBE HAD EARNED HIM AND 2 COMPAN-IONS 3 YEARS. THE OTHER 2 WERE LONG SINCE GONE, ONE FALLING IN POLAND, WHILE THE OTHER HAD DESERTED, BEEN CAUGHT AND EXECUTED.

THE REAR IS NOT THE NORMAL PLACE FOR PENAL REGIMENTS, WHOSE DUTY IS TO BE EVER TO THE FRONT AND TO WRITE THE GLORY PAGES OF HISTORY. OUR FREE TIME WE SPENT PLEASANTLY ENOUGH IN THE ZUM GOLDEN HIRSCH TAVERN, WHOSE GENIAL HOST WAS CALLED SCHULTZ OF COURSE, AND EQUALLY NATURALLY, PROVED TO BE AN OLD FRIEND OF PORTA. THE WINE WAS GOOD, THE GIRLS WILLING AND OUR SINGING WAS STRONG AT LEAST.

CHAPTER 8

CURIOSITIES OF THE BALKANS

PORTA NARROWED HIS GREEN, PIGGY EYES. - I SHALL
TELL YOU, DEAR FELLOW. IF YOU ARE A PARTY
MEMBER YOU WILL OBEY THE FÜHRER'S COMMANDMENT
THAT THE GOOD OF THE WHOLE COMES BEFORE THAT OF
THE INDIVIDUAL. AND THEREFORE, YOU WILL SAY
SOMETHING LIKE THIS: "BRAVE WARRIORS OF THE
27TH FIRE-AND-SWORD REGIMENT! TO HELP YOU TO
FIGHT EVEN BETTER FOR FÜHRER AND PEOPLE, I, IN
MY GRATITUDE, WILL MAKE YOU A GIFT OF THE
BOTTLE OF RUM THAT HERR JOSEPH PORTA, BY GOD'S
GRACE OBERGEFREITER, IN HIS INFINITE GOODNESS
WISHED TO GIVE TO MY UNWORTHY PERSON. WASN'T
THAT JUST WHAT YOU WERE WANTING TO SAY? WEREN'T
THOSE VERY WORDS TREMBLING ON THE TIP OF YOUR
TONGUE? DEAR FELLOW, WE THANK YOU FROM THE
BOTTOM OF OUR HEARTS, AND NOW YOU MAY FUCK OFF!
PORTA FLUNG OUT HIS HAND WITH A MAGNIFICENT
FLOURISH, RAISED HIS CAP AND SHOUTED, "GRÜSS
GOTT!"
AS SOON AS THE WRETCHED NAZI RAILWAYMAN HAD
GONE, FURIOUSLY GNASHING HIS TEETH, WE OPENED
THE PARCEL.
THERE WERE FIVE BOTTLES OF WINE, THERE WAS A
WHOLE ROAST OF PORK; THERE WERE TWO ROAST CHICK-
ENS, AND THERE WAS...

CHAPTER 9

DESTINATION: NORTH AFRICA

JUST LET ME GET MY HANDS ON THE THROAT OF THE
POET WHO WROTE THAT THE MEDITERRANEAN WAS BLUE
AND LOVELY AND SMILING.

WE WERE STATIONED IN NAPLES, EQUIPPED WITH BRAND-NEW TANKS AND PUT INTO TROPICAL UNIFORM.

WHEN WE EVENTUALLY EMBARKED THERE WERE 5 BATTALIONS IN TOTAL, 5000 MEN DIVIDED BETWEEN 2 SHIPS, FORMER PASSENGER STEAMERS.

EACH MAN WAS ISSUED A LIFE-BELT AND WE HAD STRICT ORDERS NEVER TO TAKE THEM OFF...BUT THEY MADE TOO GOOD PILLOWS FOR ANYONE TO RESPECT SUCH AN ORDER.

THERE WERE AA GUNS MOUNTED ON THE DECK, AND WE WERE ESCORTED BY THREE ITALIAN TORPEDO-BOATS.

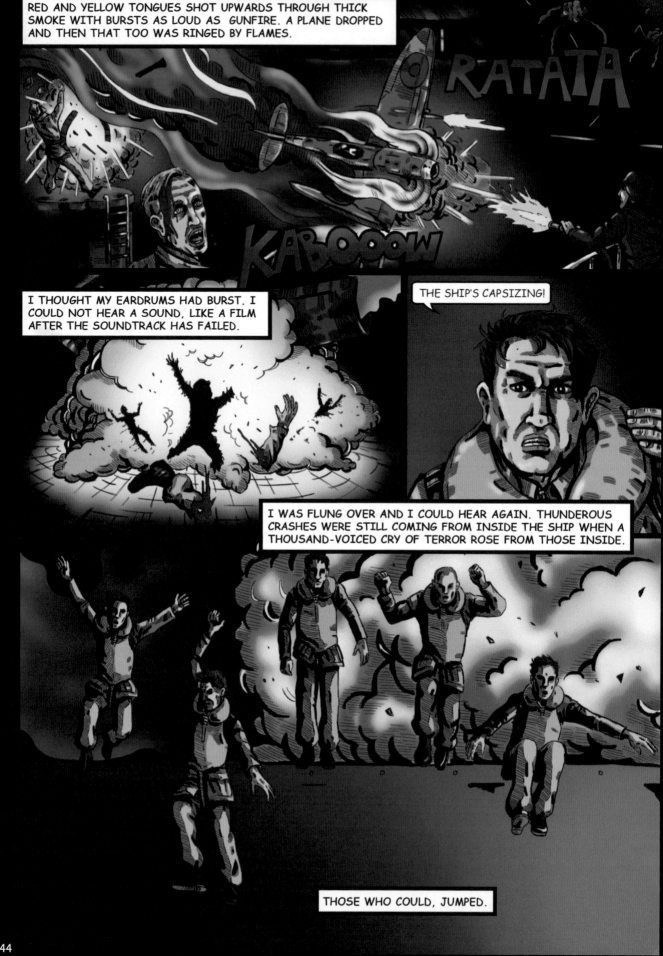

THE WATER WAS SO FANTASTICALLY FAR BENEATH ME THAT I THOUGHT I WOULD NEVER REACH IT; BUT ALL AT ONCE IT HAD CLOSED OVER ME, AND I SANK AND SANK, FEELING AS THOUGH MY BODY WAS BROKEN IN HALF.

THERE WAS A ROARING AND SEETHING IN MY EARS, AND INSIDE MY HEAD SOMETHING WAS THROBBING FASTER AND FASTER, LOUDER AND LOUDER. IN THE END, I COULD NO LONGER STAND IT. I GAVE UP. NOW, YOU'RE GOING TO DIE, I THOUGHT.

Printed in Great Britain
by Amazon